BEWARE!

Mortimer's madcap plans and crazy ideas could rub off on you!

First published in 2014 by Hodder Children's Books

Hodder Children's Books, 338 Euston Road, London, NW1 3BH
Hodder Children's Books Australia, Level 17/207 Kent Street, Sydney, NSW 2000

For Jo, Susie
and Charlie
T.H.

C.M.

A catalogue record of this book is available from the British Library.

ISBN 978 0 340 99774 1

Printed in China

Hodder Children's Books is a division of Hachette Children's Books,
an Hachette UK Company

www.hachette.co.uk

MORTYMER KEENE

KEENE

GHOSTS ON THE LOOSE

Tim Healey and Chris Mould

SAINT BARNABAS
S B
SCHOOL

Pale Rider
Age: uncertain
Special features: rides a
horse called Hades
Weak point:
no fun at parties
Favourite phrase:
'My name is Death!'

SAINT BARNABAS
S B
SCHOOL

Plague Victim
Age: 678 years
Special features:
warts, blisters, sores
Weak point: body odour
Favourite phrase:
'Unclean! Unclean!'

SAINT BARNABAS S B *SCHOOL*

Pirate
Age: 361 years
Special features:
missing body parts
Weak point:
inappropriate behaviour
Favourite phrase:
'Ooo aaarrrr!'

SAINT BARNABAS S B *SCHOOL*

Grey Lady
Age: 292 years
Special features:
grey complexion
Weak point:
always moaning
Favourite phrase:
'Alas! Alas!'

SAINT BARNABAS SCHOOL

Victorian Hangman
Age: 193 years
Special features:
heavy footsteps
Weak point:
only says one thing
Favourite phrase:
'Your time has come...'

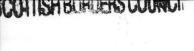

'I've just seen a ghost!'

Screamed young Mr Bevan,

The man who taught

Shakespeare to kids in Year Seven.

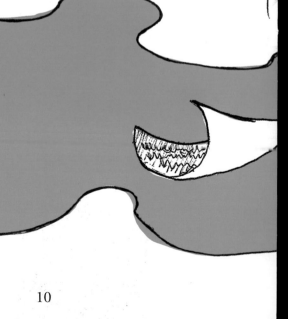

The staff room was **crowded,**
And Mrs MacNee
Was first to his side
With a hot cup of tea.

'Sit down Mr Bevan,
You don't have to shout,
Some tea and some biscuits
Will soon sort you out.'

'Look, out on the playground!'
The young teacher shrieked.
Mr Green reached the window
And through it he peeked.

Have you gone crazy?
I hope you're not drunk…'
Then he saw it too:

A HOODED BLACK MONK!

The sinister spectre
Moved silently by
With a shadowy face
And one glimmering eye.

Children were running

AND SCREAMING WITH FEAR,

Sobbing whenever
The Black Monk drew near.

Mr Field called for calm,
Mr Field called for cool:

'DON'T PANIC!
DON'T PANIC!
GET BACK INTO SCHOOL!'

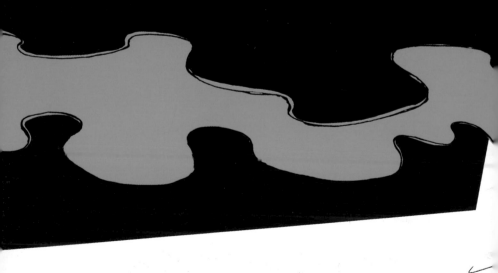

He smiled to the staff room
'I can do no more.'
Then he dropped like a log
In a faint to the floor.

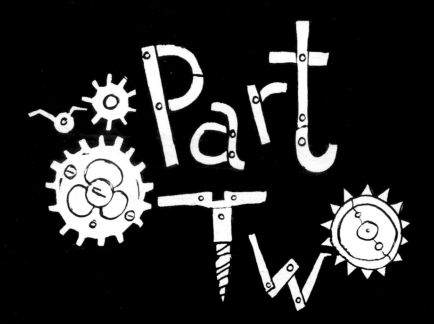

Back towards school
The pupils came fleeing,
Scarcely believing in
What they were seeing.

Then sixteen plague victims
All covered with sores
And bandaged with rags
Came out through the doors!

'Aargh!' cried Kate Moore
As the smell of their breath
Engulfed the whole playground
With the stench of Black Death.

'Ghosts in the playground!
Ghosts on the loose!
Can't somebody help us?'
Cried Emily Bruce.

Oliver Morris
Stood staring aghast
And speechless with fear
As a Pale Rider passed.

And then a Grey Lady
With never a sound,
Just eerily drifted
A foot above ground.

Jeremy Harrison
Hid in a loo.
But he locked himself in
With the Grey Lady too!

Up in the staff room
Panic was peaking;
Poor Mrs Moray could not
Hear herself speaking.

She rapped on the table
And called for some calm.
'Just possibly there is
No cause for alarm.'

'No cause for alarm?
D'you think we're all fools?'
Cried young Mr Bevan,

'The school's full

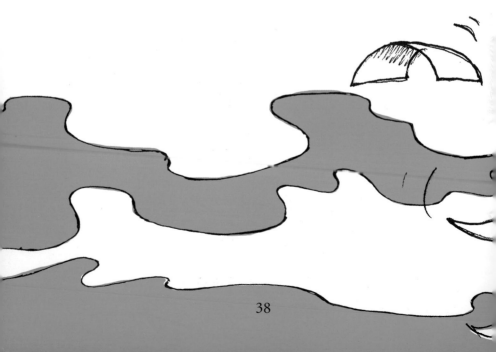

of ghouls!!!'

'Just listen a moment
And hear what I say,
There may be a culprit,'
Said Mrs Moray.

'There may be a culprit,
You know who I mean?
This may be the doing
Of Mortimer Keene!'

Up in the science lab
Mortimer Keene
Looked lovingly on
His new Phantom Machine.

'I've cracked it,' he cried,
'I've found Tunnels in Time!
"Wormholes" they call them,
Oh this is sublime!

I fix on the place and
The year and the date,
Program the laptop
And just sit and wait.

Up through the wormholes
And out through the screen
The ghosts keep on coming,'
Laughed Mortimer Keene.

Racing towards him
Wild with dismay
Came brave Mr Green
And bold Mrs Moray.

They brushed past the pirates
And burst through the door
To find Mortimer pacing
The science lab floor.

'The wonders of science!'
He mused with a smile.
'Let's save our results on
A full back-up file.'

'Don't save your results,
You daft little fool!'
Cried Mrs Moray,
'Will you please save the school!'

An ambulance siren
Wailed from the ground
Seeking poor Mr Field
Who had not yet come round.

Squad cars came too;
Policemen burst out
To see for themselves
What the screams were about.

'The whole school is haunted!'
Wailed Emily Bruce…
…A Victorian Hangman
Strolled out with his noose,

Slamming the doors
With a horrible bang,
As if he was searching
For someone to hang.

A Hangman in school!
The police were in shock.
A Hangman approaching
The school's science block!

In the laboratory
Mortimer Keene
Grew suddenly worried by
What this might mean.

'He's coming to get me…
Cripes, he draws near!'
Now, even Mortimer
Shivered with fear.

'You are right, I suppose,
I'd better act quick.
A backloop in spacetime
Might just do the trick.'

The Victorian Hangman
Stomped into the room
Bearing his noose and
The promise of doom.

'A warpdrive reversal!'
The boffin raved on,
Clicking hard on the mouse
Till the Hangman was gone.

The Hangman was gone!
Worn to a shred,
The teachers just gaped
As Mortimer said:

'Call them phantoms or ghosts,
– I have no objections –
Though technically they're just
Spacetime projections.

Plague victims next,'
He said with a grin,
Consigning them all
To the recycle bin.

The Monk, the Grey Lady
And others more weird
Sank down into the bin
And then disappeared.

Into the science lab
Teachers came creeping,
Some of them trembling,
Some softly weeping.

Into the science lab
School kids came too,
Some white as sheets
And some faintly blue.

'It's alright, it's over,
They've all gone away.
Now back to your classrooms,'
Said Mrs Moray.

Then she turned for a word
With a tired Mr Green
On the unending problem
Of Mortimer Keene.

'I've said it before
And I'll say it again,
Although he's a problem,
That boy's got a brain!'

Following these events, Mrs Moray sent
Mortimer's back-up files on spacetime
projection to the Ministry of Defence
where they remain under close scrutiny,
protected by the Official Secrets Act.
It is not known whether
any use is being made of them.

COTTISH BORDERS COUNCIL

INFORMATION SERVICE

Mortimer's
PHANTOM
MACHINE
Plan!

Mortimer Keene

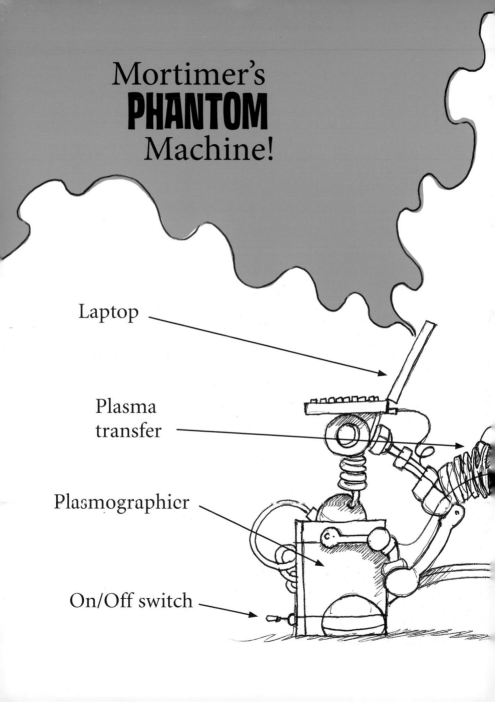

Mortimer's **PHANTOM** Machine!

Laptop

Plasma transfer

Plasmographier

On/Off switch

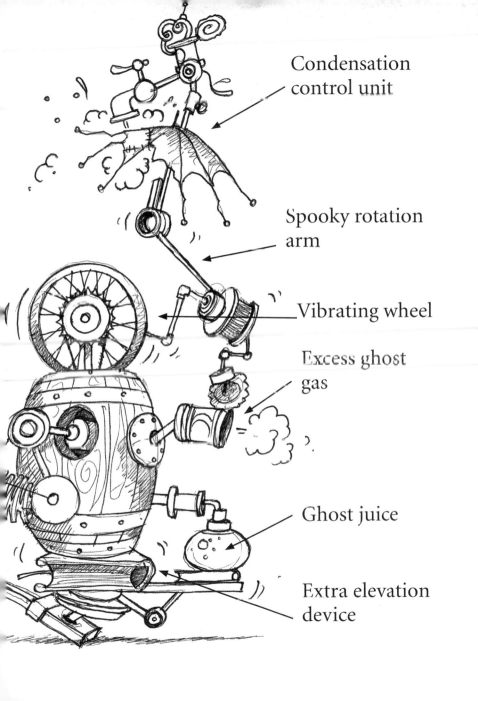

Condensation
control unit

Spooky rotation
arm

Vibrating wheel

Excess ghost
gas

Ghost juice

Extra elevation
device

A-Z of Ghosts

Apparition – anything that appears supernaturally.

Black Dog – not all ghosts are human.

Creeps – horrible tingling sensation in the flesh often experienced in the presence of a ghost (or a teacher).

Doppelgänger – ghostly double of a living person, from the German meaning 'double walker'.

Ectoplasm – misty, gloopy substance which some say ghosts are made of.

Fright mask – scary mask worn by a non-ghost.

Ghouls – creatures that haunt graveyards, drink blood and eat the dead. Not to be confused with ghosts.

Halloween – short for All Hallows' Evening. A festival held on 31st October, originally to honour the dead. Now a time for parties and spooky pranks.

Ignis fatuus – Latin for 'foolish fire'. From ancient times people have reported ghostly lights which it is foolish to follow. See also Jack-o-lantern.

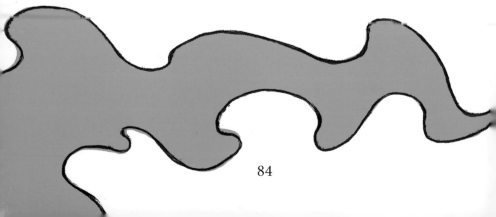

Jack-o-lantern – a type of ignis fatuus. Also, a grinning pumpkin face, carved for Halloween.

Kings – tend to haunt their old palaces.

Ladies – spooky Grey Ladies and White Ladies are said to have died of grief after being betrayed in love.

Mummies – wrapped-up bodies of ancient Egyptians who come back to life and wreak havoc.

Night – best time to see ghosts. Why don't they show up more in daytime when we could take a better look at them?

Orbs – balls of light hovering above ground are often captured by ghost hunters with cameras. Is this how ghosts travel?

Poltergeist – a ghost which moves things about but cannot actually be seen.

Queens – Anne Boleyn is the most famous phantom queen, executed by her husband Henry VIII.

Restless spirits – all ghosts are restless. They wouldn't be ghosts if they were at rest.

Scream – what ghosts make you want to do.

Tower of London – one of the most haunted castles. Has loads of royal ghosts, shadowy apparitions and even a phantom bear!

Undead – someone who is dead but not dead. Er, sort of.

Vortex – mysterious, swirling funnel shape, also known as a funnel ghost. May be felt as a cold spot in old houses.

Will-o-wisp – mischievous ghost light which lures travellers from their path in the dark. See Ignis fatuus.

X certificate – anything truly horrible

Yuk! – common response to sighting a zombie.

Zombie – grisly-looking corpse which has been brought back to life.

MORtiMER'S GHOSt HUNt

Instructions:

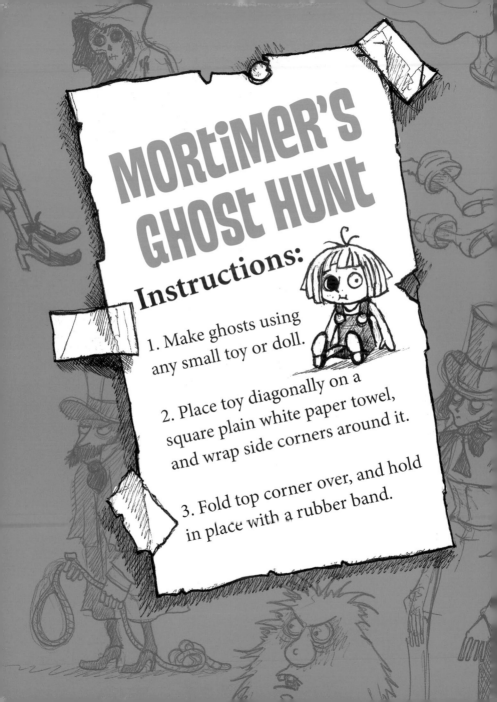

1. Make ghosts using any small toy or doll.

2. Place toy diagonally on a square plain white paper towel, and wrap side corners around it.

3. Fold top corner over, and hold in place with a rubber band.

4. Use black pen to make eyes, nose and mouth.

5. Hide ghosts in a room, always leaving corners of the spooky faces just visible.

6. Send in players one at a time. Each has 30 seconds to find a ghost.

7. The winner is the one who finds a ghost quickest!

MORTIMER'S TOP TIPS ON TELLING A GHOST STORY

- Arrange chairs for the audience in a semi-circle. When the time comes, you should stand in the centre.

- Draw the curtains and switch off the lights.

- Place a torch under your chin so it lights up your face for spooky effect. Now let the audience in.

- Your story does not have to be set in a ruined castle. Some of the creepiest are set in familiar places that everyone knows.

- Speak slowly and pause often for effect. Remember, there is nothing more eerie than silence.

- Don't be too scary or someone may faint with fright.

- If somebody faints (probably a grown-up), get them to lie on their back with their legs higher than the head.

978 0 340 99775 8